student
WORKBOOK

OCR AS Critica
Unit 1: Introduction to Critical Thinking
Jill Swale

Philip Allan, an imprint of Hodder Education, an Hachette UK company, Market Place, Deddington, Oxfordshire OX15 0SE

Orders
Bookpoint Ltd, 130 Milton Park, Abingdon, Oxfordshire OX14 4SB

tel: 01235 827827, fax: 01235 400401

e-mail: education@bookpoint.co.uk

Lines are open 9.00 a.m.–5.00 p.m., Monday to Saturday, with a 24-hour message answering service. You can also order through the Philip Allan website: www.philipallan.co.uk

© Philip Allan Publishers 2008

ISBN 978-0-340-97378-3

First printed 2008

Impression number 12

Year 2013

Printed in Spain

Hachette UK's policy is to use papers that are natural, renewable and recyclable products and made from wood grown in sustainable forests. The logging and manufacturing processes are expected to conform to the environmental regulations of the country of origin.

P02235

Introduction

This is the first of two workbooks designed to support and complement AS courses in Critical Thinking for the OCR 2008 specification. The aims of this one are to help you practise the skills required in Unit 1 of the course and to provide you with essential information and useful examples.

Section 1: The language of reasoning

This section begins with an exercise demonstrating the relevance of critical thinking to events in the news. It then introduces you to the important elements of an argument, since one of the skills tested in critical thinking is the ability to analyse reasoning (Assessment Objective 1). After learning to recognise different parts of an argument, you will encounter various types of flawed reasoning and begin to evaluate evidence. Practising these skills through a series of exercises will help you towards Assessment Objective 2, the evaluation of reasoning. This is an accumulative process, so it is advisable to tackle the exercises in the right order.

Section 2: Credibility

This section will teach you to apply the criteria used to assess the claims of individuals offering contrasting opinions or evidence about an issue or event. You will learn to evaluate the credibility of a variety of documents and visual sources and practise the techniques of identifying conflicting and corroborative evidence, learning how to reach a judgement after going through the steps of balancing, weighing and assessing the quality of evidence.

Section 3: Specimen examination paper

Once you have practised each skill, the workbook provides a full-length practice paper modelled on the specimen paper supplied by the OCR examination board, though you should **be aware that real examination papers vary a little from year to year**, so practise as many as you can. Try to complete the paper in 1 hour 30 minutes, the time allocated to the examination in this unit.

After using the workbook you should continue to practise your skills by applying them to real-life situations such as news reports, discussions in the media and debates in the classroom. Remember that the essential purpose of critical thinking is to make you more aware of the need to reason carefully about live issues that concern you in your everyday life.

We hope this workbook will help you in your studies and in your examination.

Critical thinking has become a popular subject to study because it teaches skills that are valuable in everyday life. Most of us are bombarded with media news and opinions, messages from advertisers about the excellence of their products and advice from people we meet. In Unit 1 of the OCR course you will learn to recognise and analyse arguments and assess some of their flaws and strengths. You will discover techniques that can be applied systematically to help you judge the credibility of documents, evidence and witnesses. **Credibility** means the extent to which you can believe people or evidence.

Before we start, the following exercise will demonstrate that you already have some of the skills needed to be a successful critical thinker. Read the excerpt entitled **'Mission accomplished' again?** and answer the accompanying questions.

Exercise 1

'Mission accomplished' again?

A new US war lie — concocted by the Bush administration, embraced by mainstream media — attempts to justify continuing the Iraq occupation.

It claims the 'surge' of 30,000 US troops is bringing 'peace' and 'stability' .

The *Chicago Tribune* reported Baghdad's transformation. 'Children play in parks, young women stay out after dark, restaurants are filled with families and old men sit at sidewalk cafés smoking pipes.'

But a Pew Research Center poll of US reporters working in Iraq found that 'nearly 90% of US journalists in Iraq say much of Baghdad is still too dangerous to visit' — and that many believe US media coverage 'has painted too rosy a picture'.

The US government's statistics showing decreased sectarian violence in Iraq are deceptive, according to *Washington Post* reporter Thomas Ricks, just returned from Baghdad. The city's violence 'is only back down to the 2005 level — which is like moving from the eighth circle of hell to the fifth.'

New York Times stories celebrate the 'return of normalcy' to Iraq by observing that 20,000 Iraqis have returned from Syria, where more than 2 million fled in the last 2 years. However, reporter Damien Cave suggests that 'The description of the scope of the return appears to have been massaged by politics. Under pressure to show results, the government has publicised figures that exaggerate the movement back to Iraq and Iraqis' confidence that the current lull in violence can be sustained.'

A UN survey of 110 Iraqi families leaving Syria found that 46% could not afford to stay, due to Syria's refusal to grant Iraqi refugees work visas; 25% cited problems caused by Syria's refugee entry policies; and just 14% had heard that Iraq had become safer.

Anyway, 20,000 people returning to a country of 22 million, where 4 million people have been made refugees, hardly seems cause for celebration.

The media optimism seems less a reflection of reality and more a manifestation of Bush's new justification for why the USA should stay in Iraq.

Before, we were told that US troops had to stay to keep Iraq from descending into chaos. Now, we hear it's because the occupation is working — and it would be a shame to withdraw just as military force is beginning to pay dividends.

Adapted from *Socialist Worker*, 7 December 2007 www.socialistworker.org/2007-2/655/655_02_Surge.shtml

1 What is the author implying (suggesting) by the word 'new' in the phrase 'a new US lie'?

....

....

2 What is the author's intention in punctuating the first two words of the headline and the words 'peace' and 'stability' with quotation marks?

....

....

....

....

....

3 What impression is the *Chicago Tribune* attempting to create of life in Iraq now? Discuss the intended effect of the details described.

....

....

....

....

....

....

4 Suggest reasons why the report by the *Chicago Tribune* might not be entirely credible.

....

....

....

....

....

....

5 The Pew Research Center is described as a 'non-partisan fact tank that provides information on the issues, attitudes and trends shaping America and the world through public opinion polling'. Comment on how reliable you would expect data from this source to be, explaining your answer.

6 Explain why, according to *Washington Post* reporter Thomas Ricks, US government statistics about decreased sectarian violence in Iraq could be 'deceptive' without necessarily being wrong.

7 Explain what the reporter Damien Cave meant by media descriptions of refugees returning from Syria to Iraq being 'massaged by politics'.

8 Consider the United Nations (UN) survey of reasons why refugees to Syria were returning to Iraq. How credible is the source?

9 To what extent do the findings back up the majority view in the US media that refugees returning to their homeland is a sign of 'peace' and 'stability'?

10 Compare the use of statistics in the Pew Research Center poll and the survey of returning refugees. Which source uses statistics more precisely?

11 The passage refers to 2 million Iraqi people fleeing from Iraq to Syria but later states that '4 million people have been made refugees'. Clarify this apparent contradiction.

12 Explain two reasons why '20,000 people returning to a country of 22 million, where 4 million people have been made refugees' is not a 'cause for celebration'.

13 In the final paragraph the writer implies a contradiction in US army policy concerning occupation of Iraq. Suggest two possible conclusions the reader might be expected to draw.

14 The article you have just read appeared in *Socialist Worker*, which describes itself as 'a fighting newspaper dedicated to the struggle for justice, freedom and democracy' and 'a revolutionary, anti-capitalist newspaper based in Britain'. To what extent does this information affect your interpretation of the opinions you have just read?

15 Now you have completed this analysis, write about five bullet points suggesting how critical thinkers are likely to approach media articles.

Section 1: The language of reasoning
Analysing arguments

Now you have seen the relevance of critical thinking to everyday life, it is necessary to learn some basic vocabulary. Like the *Socialist Worker* article on p. 3, many of the resources you will be analysing include **arguments**. In ordinary language, we use the word 'argument' for any disagreement. In contrast, in critical thinking an argument is a verbal attempt to persuade, giving reasons to support the conclusion. If someone expresses a view but fails to say why, strictly speaking this is not an argument. Instead it could be described as a **claim** or **assertion**.

Arguments therefore have two parts. **Reason(s) + conclusion = argument**.

Despite its name, the conclusion is not always at the end of the argument. Consider these examples, and decide which part of each sentence is the reason and which part is the conclusion.

Examples:
1 *It is important to reduce air travel because it is the fastest-growing cause of global warming.*
2 *Air travel is the fastest-growing cause of global warming, so it is important to reduce it.*

You have probably worked out that in example 1, the conclusion came first, 'It is important to reduce air travel', whereas in example 2 the similar conclusion came in the second half.

You probably used verbal clues to help you decide. Arguments are often about something that should be done or something that ought not to be allowed. Conclusions therefore often contain verbal clues such as *must, should, ought, need* or phrases such as *it is important/essential/right/wrong*.

Because they arise from a reasoning process, if they are placed at the end of the argument, conclusions are often preceded by **indicator** words such as *therefore* or *so, hence* or *thus*.

There are also indicator words signalling that reasons are being given, such as *because, as, for* and *since*. Some arguments lack these verbal clues, but could be slightly rephrased to include them. If you are unsure which part of an argument is the conclusion, try inserting the word *therefore* in various places to see where it fits most logically (the 'therefore test').

Explanations are different from arguments. They may have the same components of **reasons + conclusion**, but they are not attempting to persuade. Instead they inform people about generally uncontroversial facts. An example of an explanation is *Many mammals grow thicker fur in the winter because they need to insulate their bodies from the cold*. In contrast, an argument seems to call out for someone to put forward an opposing view, backed up by different reasons. Many news articles begin with explanations to provide background information and then move on to arguments in which the opinions of the author are presented and backed up by reasons and supporting evidence. It is important to be able to distinguish between fact and opinion.

Exercise 2

Decide which of the sentences in the table are explanations and which are arguments. Tick the appropriate boxes. Then, only for those that are arguments, underline the conclusion.

Example	Explanation	Argument
1 The Archbishop of York John Sentamu cut up his dog collar during a television interview because he wanted to convey the way President Mugabe had been 'destroying the identities' of the Zimbabwean people.		
2 As the people of Zimbabwe are starving, the international community must intervene to help them.		
3 People are starving in Zimbabwe because only one in five of the adult population is employed and basic items such as bread are often not available in local shops.		
4 Prime Minister Gordon Brown has boycotted an EU–Africa summit because of Mr Mugabe's presence.		
5 Britain ought not to intervene in the politics of African countries such as Zimbabwe because they are no longer its colonies.		
6 Some African leaders see Mr Mugabe as an important colleague and object to the idea of former colonial powers, such as the UK, intervening in African politics.		

Exercise 3

Analyse the following arguments, indicating which part is the reason and which part is the conclusion. Copy the parts into the chart on p. 10. Next, write out any indicator words or phrases, saying whether they are reason indicators or conclusion indicators.

1 People should buy fair trade bananas because growers in the developing world deserve to earn a living wage.
2 As dolphins often die in fishing nets, you ought to ensure the tuna you buy is caught with a rod.
3 Think twice before ordering pâté de foie gras. It is made from the liver of force-fed geese.
4 Mothers in developing countries often cannot access clean water so it is wrong to encourage them to buy powdered baby milk.
5 Oxfam Unwrapped should be supported as it encourages affluent people to help the developing world.
6 Your friend already has everything she needs, therefore it is better to buy a goat for Africa as her Christmas gift.
7 Parents have a duty to maintain their children's health. They must stop them eating so much heavily processed food.
8 The government needs to warn us about health risks in food since it has greater access to specialist information.
9 We ought to be free to take risks when we want to. Life is full of enjoyable risks.
10 I have worked hard for my wages, so I should be able to spend them how I want.

No.	Reason	Conclusion	Indicator words	Type
1				
2				
3				
4				
5				
6				
7				
8				
9				
10				

Assumptions

An **assumption** is an unstated part of an argument, something which is taken for granted and not mentioned directly because it seems obvious to the arguer. Sometimes assumptions are called **suppositions**. There are no indicator words preceding assumptions because they are not explicit, so they may be difficult to spot. Here is an example:

When I went to post my Christmas cards, the pillar box was so full that people could easily have helped themselves to the contents. Quite a few people may be deprived of their Christmas cheques this year.

What is the main assumption needed to make this argument work? The answer is 'There are likely to be dishonest people interested in stealing items from pillar boxes'. If the incident took place in a remote, highly religious community, this might not be the case.

Another assumption is necessary for the conclusion to be reached. It is that items in pillar boxes at Christmas frequently contain cheques. In this argument, there is only one stated reason (abbreviated to **R1**) for the conclusion (**C**), but the assumptions perform a similar function, playing an invisible yet significant role in a chain of reasoning. This chain could be written out as follows:

- *When I went to post my Christmas cards, the pillar box was so full that people could easily have helped themselves to the contents.* (R1)
- *There are likely to be dishonest people interested in stealing items from pillar boxes.* (Assumption acting as R2)
- *Items in pillar boxes at Christmas frequently contain cheques.* (Assumption acting as R3)
- *Quite a few people may be deprived of their Christmas cheques this year.* (C)

Note that for brevity it is customary to use the letter R for a reason and C for a conclusion.

One way of being certain that you have identified an assumption correctly is to apply the reverse or negative test. By changing the assumption to its opposite (e.g. *There are not likely to be dishonest people interested in stealing items from pillar boxes*), you should find that the conclusion can no longer be reached.

Note that many assumptions are reasonable ones to make, so they do not necessarily weaken arguments. The assumption that items in pillar boxes at Christmas frequently contain cheques is one most people would accept as **sound**, **safe** or **justified**.

However, on other occasions arguers make **false** or **unjustified** assumptions and it is particularly important to identify these as **flaws** in the reasoning. It is useful when commenting on these to indicate alternative possibilities by using the word *whereas* as follows:

The argument assumes that … whereas it is possible that …

Exercise 4

Identify the most crucial assumptions in the following arguments and write them below. Sometimes there is more than one assumption.

1 My friend is delighted that she has just acquired two cats. She won't be so pleased when she finds her house full of kittens.

....
....
....

2 The population is ageing markedly. Public libraries should increase their stock of large print books.

....
....
....

3 The Tesco car park is quite full. There must be lots of people shopping in the supermarket today.

....
....
....

4 Anne's son has just been accepted for university. She will be proud to have a graduate in the family.

....
....
....

5 In our school tests in French and German the girls scored higher marks on average than the boys for the third year running. Girls clearly have a greater aptitude for modern foreign languages than boys.

....
....
....

Assessing assumptions

As well as identifying assumptions, you may be required to assess them and to explain why you consider they are reasonable or unreasonable ones to make. This will involve examining the type of assumption being made. Does it assume some factual point and, if so, how easy would it be to access the relevant evidence? The example below is of this type.

The population is ageing markedly. Public libraries should increase their stock of large print books.

Scientific evidence can easily be found suggesting that eyesight does tend to deteriorate with age. Research could be conducted to establish whether a significant proportion of elderly people use the large print books in public libraries and whether they consider the stocks are adequate to meet their needs. You could write that the soundness of this assumption could therefore be checked but that the information was not presented in the passage.

Alternatively the assumption might be based on an opinion. Here is an example.

I've worked really hard all year. Despite global warming, I'm entitled to my holiday flight to a tropical island.

The main assumptions here are as follows:

People who work hard are entitled to the holiday of their choice. This entitlement to holiday flights should override concerns for the environment associated with air travel.

Whether you accept these assumptions will depend on your own moral outlook. Unit 3 will teach you about ethical reasoning, but for Unit 1 it would be sufficient to write that the reasonableness of this assumption is not easy to establish because it is based on opinion, not fact. You might also observe that the assumption:

People who work hard are entitled to the holiday of their choice.

is based on a principle. A **principle** is a general statement, often about how people ought to behave or how things should be. It is intended to be a rule that can be applied in a wide range of situations. Some principles are established by wide consensus, but all moral principles are a matter of opinion, not fact.

Sometimes assumptions are based on speculations about future events. Look at this example from exercise 4:

Anne's son has just been accepted for university. She will be proud to have a graduate in the family.

This is an example of **hypothetical reasoning**, which is often worded using the grammatical structure 'if X then Y'. The assumption is based on the reasoning:

If Anne's son has been accepted, then he will be awarded a degree.

As we can never predict people's future with certainty, assumptions based on hypothetical reasoning should be assessed as unsafe. Nevertheless, life experience or research may provide some idea of the probability of the predicted events occurring, so it might be possible to estimate the extent to which the assumption is a reasonable one to make. In this case, as recent figures suggest that about 16% of higher education students drop out of their courses, it is not a safe assumption.

Exercise 5

Identify the most crucial assumptions in each of the following arguments and write them below. State whether the assumption being made is based on fact, opinion, a principle or hypothetical reasoning and assess the extent to which you think the assumption is reasonable and explain your answer.

1 Only 19% of Somali immigrants to the UK are employed. The public tax bill for unemployment benefits for this group must be enormous.

Assumption

....

....

Type

....

Assessment and explanation

....

....

....

....

2 Somalis living in Britain are largely refugees and asylum seekers. In such a case, it would be irrelevant if the cost of supporting them exceeded the benefits they brought to the economy.

Assumption

....

....

Type

....

Assessment and explanation

....

....

....

....

3 We should not be unduly gloomy if some new immigrant groups are contributing poorly to Britain's economy at the moment. The children of Chinese and Indian immigrants are performing exceptionally well in our education system and are destined for well-paid and valuable careers.

Assumption

....

....

Type

....

Assessment and explanation

....

....

....

....

4 Polish immigrants to Britain earn on average only £7.30 an hour compared with the average wage of the native UK worker of £11.10. Something should be done about the way Polish workers are threatening the employment of British workers by undercutting wages.

Assumption

....

....

Type

....

Assessment and explanation

....

....

....

....

5 While only 34% of UK-born people work in the public services, such as education and healthcare, this is the case for 48% of immigrants from Somalia, 50% from Nigeria and 60% from the Philippines. Clearly these immigrant groups are more useful to us than a lot of British-born people.

Assumption

....

....

Type

....

Assessment and explanation

....

....

....

....

Counter-arguments and counter-assertions

To complete our study of the structure of arguments, you need to be able to recognise a **counter-argument (CA)**. This is an argument that takes an opposing view to the main one being expressed. In a long passage, the writer might take one line of argument, and then interrupt it to discuss an opposing view. The reasons supporting this are likely to be briefly indicated then their weaknesses pointed out. Having dismissed potential opposition, the arguer then continues with the main argument.

A **counter-claim** (**CC**) or **counter-assertion** is similar and in some contexts you may find the words 'counter-assertions', 'counter-claims' and 'counter-arguments' used interchangeably. Strictly speaking though, counter-claims or counter-assertions challenge the main argument without providing any supporting reasons. They tend to be brief as a result, often consisting of a phrase such as 'Although many people believe X,…'.

If you remember that an argument has to have reasons as well as a conclusion, whereas a conclusion alone is called an assertion or claim, you should be able to distinguish counter-arguments from counter-assertions.

As either a counter-argument or a counter-assertion occurs within an argument that is predominantly working in the opposite direction, it is likely to be met swiftly with a **challenge** or response. **Response to the counter-argument** can be abbreviated as **RCA** and **response to the counter-claim** by **RCC**.

A **counter-example** is one that appears to provide evidence against the main thrust of the argument. For example, if you were arguing for the importance of access to books for every child, blind children would be a counter-example, as auditory materials would better meet their needs.

You will need to be able to identify these components of arguments in Unit 1. For Unit 2 you will need to include them in arguments you write yourself.

Exercise 6

Look at the arguments below and underline the counter-arguments or counter-claims and the responses or challenges to them, distinguishing the components by annotating the underlined sections in the margins with the letters 'CA', 'CC' and 'RCA' or 'RCC'.

1 Despite the suggestion that the communication techniques of MPs have become professionalised, there is enormous variation in how frequently MPs express their views in the media and how competently they do so. Often they have to retract what they have said when members of the public object to offensive remarks. All MPs ought to be trained to deliver their messages articulately and with discretion.

2 Everyone should have a computer. They are the most efficient way of accessing virtually every fact you want to know almost in an instant. Because of the existence of internet cafés, it is possible to communicate by e-mail or use the internet without owning a computer. However, this can be expensive and often inconvenient. Having your own machine enables you to record everything you wish to remember, check train times before rushing out of the house, and listen to music or missed radio shows in the comfort of your own living room.

3 You only have to stand behind someone in a supermarket queue to see how much junk food many people buy. It is often said that the public are eating more healthily now, but this is yet another media myth. Children avoid healthy school dinners and cinema-goers seem unable to watch a film without gorging themselves on popcorn, even though most of them have probably just had dinner. If we want to avoid an increasing obesity crisis, the government must plan a much more effective healthy eating campaign.

4 Many people oppose capital punishment for murder because they regard it as inhumane and worry that it is irreversible if there is a miscarriage of justice. Murder is inhumane and miscarriages of justice are very rare. Prison these days can be relatively comfortable and, in any case, prisons are overcrowded, so we need to find alternative forms of punishment. In the wake of the spate of killings of young people by ruthless villains who apparently have no fear of prison, we need to consider bringing back the death penalty for murder.

5 Many people worry about how to invest their savings. Stocks and shares are an attractive option as they can bring high returns. However, they can also result in heavy losses. Cash ISAs provide reasonable interest rates which are tax free and the investments are much more secure. People who want to be sure of a reasonable steady income from their savings would be well advised to invest in Cash ISAs.

Distinguishing reasons from evidence and examples

The arguments we have examined so far have only consisted of a few sentences. The conclusions of longer arguments are usually drawn from a number of reasons (**R1**, **R2**, **R3** etc.), each of which may be supported by evidence (**EV**) and examples (**EX**). If asked to identify the reasons on which a conclusion is based, make sure you look for these main points rather than being distracted by the details that support them. Think of the reasoning involved as a series of steps or levels in a hierarchy. Examples and evidence such as research data are amassed to support reasons. Then usually several of these reasons combine to support a conclusion.

Exercise 7

Read the argument in the following box. Each of its nine sentences has been numbered and set out on a new line to help you answer the questions that follow.

Getting it all in proportion

1 Reading the papers, you would think that air travel is the biggest cause of global warming and the main issue we need to tackle.

2 In fact, air travel accounts for less than 5% of carbon dioxide emissions.

3   If you really want to target the biggest culprits then look to our power stations.

4   Our largest coal-fired power station wastes two-thirds of the energy that it generates.

5   We also need to tackle the environmental damage caused by our homes.

6   These account for near to 25% of emissions.

7   However, aviation is the fastest-growing cause of global warming.

8   The amount of carbon dioxide emitted by air travel doubled between 1990 and 2004.

9   In seeking to reduce our emissions we need to examine and reassess our entire lifestyles.

Adapted from Responsible Travel www.responsibletravel.com/Copy/Copy101993.htm

1 Identify the conclusion of the argument by giving its number.

2 Identify the counter-assertion by number.

3 Identify the response to the counter-assertion by number.

4 Write down the numbers of all the reasons.

5 Write down the numbers of the evidence and examples that support the reasons.

It is not always so easy to distinguish reasons from evidence or examples, as they may be merged in the same sentence. Evidence sometimes precedes the reason it supports and sometimes follows it. For example, in a long argument about why a school needed extra funding for after-hours revision sessions, a number of reasons might be given, including the following:

We need extra time to teach students to check the accuracy of their work, such as spelling and punctuation, as the examiners' report of 2007 criticised these.

This sentence combines reason, examples and evidence. If asked to pick out reasons from the whole argument, you would only select the following:

We need extra time to teach students to check the accuracy of their work.

Tip: When picking out reasons or any other components from a passage, do not rephrase them, as this can change their meaning subtly and lose you marks. Only rephrase slightly if it is necessary to make complete sense of what you have written, for example by changing pronouns such as 'it' and 'they' to the nouns they refer to.

Exercise 8

Read the argument and fill in the answers below.

> The City of London's wealth came from the slave trade, so we owe the descendants of slaves (and African nations in general) some compensation.
>
> Apologies, such as the statement of regret issued by Tony Blair, show good will but are not enough. Many children know little about the history of slavery, so an education campaign would be useful in raising awareness. In addition, the colonial powers that most benefited from the slave trade, including the UK, should act to end African debt and dependence on the industrialised world. For every £1 that our government spends on development, Africa currently pays back £6 in servicing debt. Only by taking significant action can Britain make amends for its part in the transatlantic slave trade, which was abolished two centuries ago.

1 The conclusion of the argument is:

....

....

....

2 The reasons are:

....

....

....

....

....

....

An argument's purpose is to use reasons to make the reader or listener accept a conclusion. This may be done by **hypothetical reasoning**, often using the *if...then* construction or similar phrasing to make suppositions about the past or future.

If Columbus had not discovered America, then the Iraq war would not have happened and so many soldiers would not have died.

It is fairly clear to see that conjecturing about how past events might have turned out differently can never produce a convincing argument, as any number of other factors could also have been different.

Alternatively, arguments can be supported by reasons in the form of **personal opinions** and **moral principles**. In such cases it may be easy to detect weaknesses in the argument because the points made are **subjective** (depending on point of view). The principle

We should always be kind to animals.

would not necessarily be accepted by someone engaged in animal research that was considered essential to fight human diseases.

Of course, some reasons are simply based on incorrect facts or may be so contrary to common sense as not to be **reasonable**. Evidence may not be **plausible** or **credible** (believable) because the witnesses involved are not **reliable** (trustworthy and unmotivated to lie).

On the other hand, reasons might appear to have a factual basis, backed by evidence such as statistics, graphs or photographs, results of surveys or studies and the views of experts. Nevertheless, these still need to be treated with caution as the evidence may be presented **selectively**. The writer may provide only the data supporting his or her own view, withholding **counter-examples**.

He or she may generalise from a small sample, suggesting the data have wider **significance** than they really have. An **inadequate** reason may supply some backing for the claim, but not sufficient to show that what is claimed is definitely or always true. A simple example is:

My friend and I found the critical thinking examination harder than practice papers, so the expectation of the examiners must have been higher this year.

The conclusion is said to be **overdrawn**, as it is made too hastily on the basis of the evidence of two students. If, on the other hand, the majority of candidates nationwide found the examination harder than in previous years, the examination board might regard this as **adequate** evidence that their expectations had been too high and decide to lower the grade boundaries.

For an argument to be strong, reasons and evidence must provide sufficient support for the conclusion. They need to be both adequate and **relevant**. An **irrelevant** reason may appear to be more closely connected with the issue than it really is. It actually makes no difference to the situation.

Reasons are always put forward as being true, but on examination may prove to be unconvincing, illogical or **inconsistent** with other reasons and evidence within the same argument. Occasionally you may encounter the word **premise** instead of reason. Its meaning is virtually the same: a proposition or piece of evidence the arguer believes to be true, upon which an argument is based or from which a conclusion is drawn. The role of the critical thinker is to examine reasons and evidence carefully to see whether they are really strong enough to support the conclusion.

Exercise 9

Assess the evidence in each of the following arguments, using some of the key words discussed above.

1 My mother has bought me a birthday present! I saw her hiding something as I came in.

2 There are five boys called Daniel in my 10-year-old's class. 'Daniel' must have been an extremely fashionable name 10 years ago.

3 Jane is unlikely to be a good driver. She has little understanding of how a car engine works.

4 Robin clearly has a wide French vocabulary. In the restaurant he understood the French words for almost everything on the menu.

....

....

....

....

5 Research shows that chocolate reduces anxiety and triggers a positive mood, so the more of it I eat, the happier I'll be.

....

....

....

....

Evidence from research

Many arguments are based on evidence from research which initially sounds convincing. In the examination you may be asked to evaluate the strengths or weaknesses of such evidence. Some of the aspects you should consider are discussed below.

Sample size

If only a small number of people were asked their opinion, it is unlikely that a full range of opinions has been recorded.

Representativeness of sample

A sample might be very large yet still not reflect the views of people from many different backgrounds. To choose a **representative** sample, the researcher has to decide what attributes of potential interviewees would be likely to impact on their experience or opinions about the topic in question. These are often age, gender, social class and ethnicity, but if, for example, it was a veterinary survey of pet owners, a range of different types of pets would be needed. Once a detailed picture is obtained of the whole target population, the researcher should then choose a representative sample of respondents reflecting all these different subgroups **in the correct proportions**. Using volunteers, personal acquaintances or people in the street is unlikely to generate a representative sample.

Circumstances in which evidence is collected

Professional researchers try to collect their data in carefully **controlled conditions**, but amateurs may be happy to interview people with others listening. 'Cold callers' telephone people at home who are often too busy to answer thoughtfully. To be **valid**, data have to reflect a true picture of

the situation being studied. This means that the respondent must fully understand the questions, take them seriously and be motivated to tell the truth.

Relevance

It is important to check that any research data being used to support a conclusion are **recent** and **relevant** to the location, types of people and situation being discussed. US research on eating habits might not necessarily be helpful in tackling the UK obesity problem.

Ambiguity of findings

Research results are sometimes interpreted in a way that fits the expectation of the researcher. For example, until recently it was assumed that obesity had little to do with sugar intake because obese people claimed not to eat much sugar. However, recent experiments comparing urine tests with people's own accounts of what they ate showed that obese people generally did eat more sugar than slimmer people but underestimated it in their reports. Excess sugar is likely to be a major cause of obesity after all.

This example suggests that the connection between a piece of evidence and a conclusion is not necessarily clear cut. Data apparently supporting one contention can sometimes be viewed in a different way and used to support a different conclusion. The evidence from the obese people's reports was **ambiguous** — capable of being interpreted in more than one way.

Ambiguity can also refer to the use of words with more than one possible meaning, leading to misunderstandings or lack of clarity.

Interpretation of statistics

Researchers rarely publish all the raw statistics they have collected, preferring to process them so readers can understand the general trends. However, different ways of presenting figures can create differing impressions. A teacher might be keener to say that the **mode** of her class was grade B at AS than to say that the grades **ranged** from grade A to fail. The mode is the most common score. Alternatively, the teacher might choose to publish the **mean** mark, commonly called the average, or the **median** mark (the one in the middle of the range), depending on which one turned out to be higher. In a similar way, researchers often choose a form of statistical presentation of their data that best supports their argument so, as always, it is important for the critical thinker to be wary.

Exercise 10

Read the article below and answer the questions that follow.

Suppressing food cravings boosts consumption

Trying to cut out all thoughts of your favourite, fattening food may actually make you eat more, claims research.

Women who tried to stop thinking about chocolate ate 50% more than those who were encouraged to talk about their cravings.

This 'rebound' effect could also apply to smokers, say the Hertfordshire University authors in *Appetite* journal.

Dr James Erskine, who led the project, recruited 134 students who were asked to either suppress all thoughts about chocolate, or talk about how much they liked it.

They were then asked to choose from two brands of chocolate, believing that it was this choice that was being recorded by the researchers. However, the quantity they ate was recorded instead.

Women who had tried to suppress their cravings ate on average eight chocolates, while those who had talked freely about it ate five.

Men did not show the same effect, with the group told to talk about the snack eating more.

Dr Erskine said: 'There is a lot of research into the idea that when you suppress a thought you end up thinking about it more. However, this the first concrete evidence of how this works in relation to food choices.'

He said that the best advice to people trying to cut down on a 'sinful' food was not to avoid it completely.

Adapted from 'BBC News' website Monday, 22 October 2007 http://news.bbc.co.uk/2/hi/health/7056330.stm

1 Assess the sample used in the experiment, suggesting whether you consider it was fit for purpose.

2 Compare the headline with the first sentence. In what significant way do they differ?

3 The participants 'were asked to either suppress all thoughts about chocolate, or talk about how much they liked it.' This is rather ambiguous. What are the two possible meanings and what difference might this have made to the effectiveness of the experiment?

4 Summarise the difference between the male and the female participants' response.

....

....

....

....

....

5 Do you consider the data collected are adequate support for the conclusion in the headline? Explain your answer.

....

....

....

....

6 Comment on the use of statistics in the article.

....

....

....

....

7 Identify two strengths of the experiment, referring to methods used and the personnel conducting it.

....

....

....

....

....

....

8 How convincing do you find the suggestion that the same effect could also apply to smokers?

....

....

....

....

9 To what extent do you consider data collected in these circumstances allow us to draw firm conclusions about how people respond to cravings in their everyday lives?

....

....

....

....

....

....

The second section of the AS paper requires you to examine contrasting views or **claims** and decide which is the most **plausible** or **credible** (believable) using a number of **criteria**. A **criterion** is a test or rule on which a judgement or decision can be based. The texts may be contrasting accounts of real-life incidents from witnesses and other interested parties or they could be different expressions of opinion about an issue. There is likely to be some accompanying visual material. The criteria you are expected to apply include those outlined below.

Circumstances. Do details of the time, conditions, place or any evidence left behind at the scene provide clues about what might have happened or what might be true? Examples include traces of DNA, fingerprints, footprints and **circumstantial evidence** of the type found in detective stories. **Context** is a similar concept. You might be more inclined to believe a charge of drug-taking against a respectable politician if it took place in the 'Swinging Sixties' or accept that a usually careful driver was likely to be guilty of speeding if he was taking his wife to hospital to give birth. These last two examples involve **inductive** reasoning, meaning that claims are based on likelihood rather than absolute proof. Some types of evidence, such as DNA and fingerprints, are more conclusive than others.

Reputation. This criterion involves assessing how likely the witness or person making the claim is to be telling the truth as he or she perceives it. The passage may mention that he or she has already been in trouble with the law, has been responsible for previous accidents or has an exemplary character. If nothing is known about the individual's previous history, suppositions can be based on group membership or role. He or she may be a member of a profession with a high reputation for credibility, such as the church or criminal justice system. People are likely to tell the truth if being found not to do so would cost them their career.

Ability to see or perceive. Was the person present when the incidents under consideration occurred, or did he or she gain information from others, known as **secondary sources**? Is his or her evidence based merely on **hearsay**, rumour circulating from an unknown source, the shakiest of evidence not usually regarded as significant in court? Important evidence is supplied by **eyewitnesses**, but they are not always reliable. Even if they are neutral, with no intention to mislead, they may be mistaken about exactly what they saw. There may have been poor conditions, such as mist or bad light, distractions or obstacles. Evidence from technology such as CCTV cameras, videos, mobile phone photographs and sound recordings are included under this heading, and again it is necessary to consider the accuracy of the image or recording, whether it could have been manipulated or is open to different interpretations.

Vested interest. Individual witnesses may have something to gain by providing incomplete or inaccurate information. They may wish to avoid implicating themselves in a crime or accident where being found guilty would lead to punishment or loss of reputation or livelihood. Alternatively, their motive may be personal gain, such as compensation. Those writing for publication have a vested interest in making their material intriguing enough to sell, though on the other hand their career might be jeopardised if they falsify material. Likewise, people in a position of trust would have a vested interest in telling the truth, as to be found lying would ruin their reputation.

Expertise. Consider whether the person making the claim is likely to have adequate knowledge and experience of the relevant area. Children may be unreliable witnesses if asked to estimate how fast a car was going or how tall a person was, whereas a police officer could be expected to have a better than average ability to make such judgements.

Neutrality. Consider whether the claimant has any emotional involvement with the case. This might include favouring one side more than the other because of relationships, religious or political beliefs or nationality. An obvious example of **bias** (lack of neutrality) would be a wife giving evidence concerning some action of her husband. Someone with a bias might be tempted to lie or to offer only selective facts that support a particular case. If the evidence depends on opinion, such as how hard a colleague is working or how guilty a person looks, this information is so **subjective** that it could easily be influenced by personal bias if a particularly positive or negative relationship exists between the people involved. In contrast, the judge in a court case should have no connections with either the defendant or the accused and would try to be neutral, summing up the evidence on both sides in order to help jury members make up their minds **objectively.**

You might wish to memorise these six criteria with the mnemonic **CRAVEN**, which means cowardly.

As well as assessing the credibility of individuals and documents, you will need to compare them. You may be asked to find examples of **corroboration** — significant details on which witnesses or spokespeople agree. In addition, you will need to identify **conflict** or **inconsistency** within or between different accounts. In each case you should briefly quote or summarise the relevant details and make the source clear. It may be necessary to state explicitly that corroboration tends to increase the credibility of the relevant claimants, while inconsistency weakens it.

Reaching a judgement about credibility

Having used specific criteria to judge the credibility of individuals or documents, you may be required to form a reasoned judgement as to which is the most credible. If there are several sources supporting each side of an argument, you could show the **balance** of views by making a list in two columns of all the witnesses and sources that support each side, heading each column appropriately. There might also be a **problematic** source providing evidence that falls somewhere in between, supporting some aspects of evidence on both sides or contradicting both. This should be explained. Count the number of sources supporting each side and briefly but explicitly state which side has the greater support. This is known as the **weight** of evidence. Remember to mention the problems caused in the calculation by sources that fail to support either side.

Whether you are examining the evidence from a number of claimants or only comparing two, you will need to assess the **quality** of the evidence. This means revisiting relevant credibility criteria such as expertise, reputation or neutrality, focusing on one or two that you consider make a significant difference to how you view the claims of the opposing parties. Finally, your

judgement should be given briefly. There is no 'correct' answer, but it must follow logically from the evaluations you have already made.

The following exercises will help you to apply these criteria and skills.

Exercise 11

Read Documents 1–4 and then answer the questions that follow.

Document 1: Letter to local council from car driver Miss Jane Burrows

To whom it may concern

RE: Appeal against parking fine

I am writing to appeal against the fine I was given this morning, Tuesday 12th September on Nutley Terrace for parking after 9 a.m. I was fined for the time when I was speaking to the parking attendant, between 9:00 and 9:03 a.m. and think it grossly unfair that I should be asked to pay when I was back on Nutley Terrace at 9 a.m.

I left my car in the residents-only bay as I was teaching at Southway International School. I had to collect a pass to park in their yard from the school reception before they would let me in. The school is on the corner of Nutley Terrace. I was given the pass at 8.55 a.m. and returned immediately to Nutley Terrace (for confirmation, please speak to Mr John Morris at Southway International School: 020 100 2000).

On arriving on the terrace at 9:00 I saw the parking attendant was approaching the car, so I called out and ran to the vehicle. She ignored my calls and began to enter the information into her computer. I asked her to stop as it was 9:00 and I was ready to get back in the car.

The parking attendant then proceeded to talk to me for several minutes about why it was inadvisable to park in a residents' bay and why I should attempt to arrive significantly before the cut-off time in order to avoid penalties. She then returned to her computer and entered my information into the machine. I again asked her to stop writing, and she said that, as she had begun, she wouldn't stop. By the end of this discussion the time was 9:03. I reminded her that I had arrived several minutes earlier and she told me not to worry, and to write in to stop the fine. This seemed ridiculous as she could so easily have stopped writing in any of the preceding minutes.

She then told me that the fine was only £40, and that it was much easier for me to write in than for her to cancel the fine. She advised me to write in as soon as possible and tell you the circumstances. You can imagine I was later shocked to find she had misinformed me and the fine was in fact £120 or £60 if paid quickly. I consider even £40 to be a great deal of money, having only recently qualified as a teacher, with my student debts not yet paid off.

Since even the parking attendant agreed that I would be justified in asking for exemption, I hope that you will withdraw my fine. The circumstances are entirely unfair and I was shocked to be fined at all, let alone given the wrong information by the attendant. On phoning the helpline this morning I was advised that it was likely the fine could be retracted if I appealed in writing. I was specifically advised that I should have driven away rather than staying and listening to the attendant, allowing her to complete the paperwork, as the fine would therefore have been invalid. However, I stayed to listen to her time-consuming comments as I thought it rude, and possibly illegal, to drive off.

Yours sincerely
Jane Burrows

Document 2: Letter from the council to the car owner

Dear Miss Burrows

Thank you for your letter. This Penalty Charge Notice was issued because your vehicle was observed parked in a residents-only bay without displaying a valid resident's permit during controlled hours, which begin at 9 a.m.

In your letter you have stated that the parking attendant told you that the charge would be £40 and that you spoke to the parking attendant from 9 a.m., when you arrived at your vehicle, until 9.03 a.m., when the Penalty Charge Notice was issued. Please be advised that the parking attendant has recorded that the driver was not seen. I have also enclosed photographs taken by the parking attendant at the time, which are timed between 9.03 and 9.04, which do not show any sign of the driver.

Hence there are discrepancies between your version of events and the information supplied to the Council by the parking attendant. In such cases the Council must rely on the parking attendant's report. The parking attendant's notes were made contemporaneously with the enforcement action, not recollected weeks after the event.

For the reasons outlined above I am satisfied a contravention occurred. We will accept a £60 fine if received within 14 days. After this the fine will be £120.

Yours sincerely
Mary Bailey, Council correspondence officer

Document 3: Additional information

On receiving the above letter Jane Burrows rang the council to insist on her version of events, saying that she was absent from the photograph of her car because the parking attendant had asked her to step out of the photograph so the registration number could be seen. She was advised that if she decided to challenge the ruling, the resulting delay would result in the fine mounting to a higher figure. She decided to pay the fine.

Document 4: Parking in London

An insight into the pressures on Council Parking Attendants
- In my many discussions with them, I have come to understand that Council Parking Attendants are caught between revenue-driven pressure from the Council to issue tickets and angry drivers who believe parking enforcement should be fair and carried out with common sense.
- The Council views parking enforcement as a good source of revenue. Keeping traffic flowing is not the primary motivation. Supervisors push PAs to issue as many tickets as possible and, if they see illegally parked vehicles that have not been issued with Penalty Charge Notices, this could result in disciplinary action against PAs. These pressures result in PAs occasionally issuing illegal tickets, and in misleading uninformed members of the public about their rights in order to achieve their targets. Westminster Council acknowledges that NCP operates a performance bonus scheme for PAs but details are not yet known.

What Council Parking Services need to do
- Stop overzealous enforcement of parking rules, which can result in 30% of fines being dropped on appeal.
- Pay PAs a reasonable weekly wage instead of rewarding them for issuing tickets. Schemes described in the *Evening Standard* and *The Times,* where PAs achieving targets receive bonuses or Argos points, are unacceptable.

● Instruct PAs to cancel a Penalty Charge Notice if a motorist arrives while a PCN is being issued. It is a wretched sight to watch a PA issuing a ticket to a stunned driver, especially when the PA refuses to explain why they are issuing the ticket and fails to inform the driver of their right to drive off, with misleading statements like 'I am sorry you are too late; I cannot cancel the ticket'. Instead, the PA should say 'You are just in time; if you leave before I have attached the PCN to your car I will have my supervisor cancel the ticket according to proper procedure.'

Adapted from Parking in London website **www.doc.ic.ac.uk/~wjk/parking.html**

1 Identify the circumstantial evidence against the motorist's version of events, noting the document in which it is mentioned.

....

....

....

2 Explain how information in Document 3, if credible, may undermine this circumstantial evidence.

....

....

....

3 Assess the parties concerned (the motorist, parking attendant and council representative) using the criterion of reputation.

....

....

....

....

....

4 Assess the three parties concerned using the criterion of ability to see.

....

....

....

5 Assess the three parties concerned using the criterion of vested interest.

6 Assess Document 4 using the criteria of expertise and neutrality.

7 Suggest two different possibilities **about Jane Burrows** which might explain why she claimed she had been told the fine was only £40 when it was actually £60.

8 Suggest two alternative suppositions that could be made **about the parking attendant** to explain her telling Jane Burrows the parking fine was only £40.

9 Some of Jane Burrows' other evidence (besides the amount of the parking fine) is challenged by Document 2. Identify any evidence from elsewhere that could be used to corroborate or undermine her claims.

10 Write an overview of about six sentences balancing, weighing and assessing the quality of the evidence on either side of the controversy and reaching a final judgement about whether Jane Burrows should have been fined for parking illegally.

....

....

....

....

....

....

....

....

....

....

Reputation of sources

In the examination you are likely to encounter reports from different newspapers, websites and other media. You will need to consider the reputation of these media to judge the plausibility and reasonableness of their claims. It is useful to know whether particular British newspapers are regarded as **popular** or **quality** papers. The popular ones were until recently known as **tabloids** because of their small A3-size pages, contrasting with the larger A2-size pages of the quality **broadsheets**. However, some quality papers now appear in a smaller format, so it is necessary to assess newspapers according to content rather than size. Popular papers are more inclined to sensationalise and oversimplify news, presenting facts and opinions selectively. Their focus is often on media personalities and bizarre experiences of ordinary people. In contrast, the **serious press** provides more detail of political, economic and social issues, aiming at a more educated readership. On the whole this means quality papers are likely to carry stories which are more balanced, with less recourse to heavily **loaded language**.

Nevertheless, neither popular nor quality newspapers are politically **neutral**. Some, such as the *Guardian* and the *Daily Mirror*, are somewhat left-wing, tending to promote the rights of poorer people and minorities, and favouring nationalised industries, comprehensive schools and the welfare state. Others, such as the *Telegraph*, *Sunday Times* and *Daily Mail*, are rather right-wing, supporting business interests and taking a traditional line on issues such as grammar schools, the family and immigration.

In addition, bear in mind that British media are restricted as to what they can say about security and defence matters and will usually support national interests in the case of a dispute with another country, as is the case for media of all nations. The BBC has the reputation for presenting a **balanced** picture by inviting supporters of both sides of a controversy to express their views. However, critics suggest that it has a moderate **agenda**, avoiding interviewing people with extreme views.

The reputation of websites varies a great deal and needs to be considered. Websites may be professional ones, such as those produced by newspapers, government agencies, universities and major non-governmental agencies such as Oxfam. At the other extreme are amateurish websites set up by individuals with a particular interest or point of view. The quality of the spelling, grammar and use of loaded language can sometimes be a useful clue. The URL can provide clues as to whether the source is academic (.ac.uk here or .edu in the USA), commercial (.co.uk here or .com elsewhere) or military (.mod.uk here or .mil in the USA).

In contrast to mass media, **personal documents** such as letters, diaries and testimonies collected by historians present the experiences or views of individuals. These may be selective and are inevitably biased but they may still provide valuable insights into life in particular times and places, so they are sometimes published for the interest of the general public. Fiction too, such as the novels of Charles Dickens and Thomas Hardy, may be informative about social conditions and attitudes, though it is difficult to assess how much is exaggerated to create an effective storyline.

Exercise 12

Read Documents 1 and 2 below and then answer the questions that follow.

Document 1: Brown values Britishness

Gordon Brown promised yesterday to launch a drive to train thousands of unemployed workers for jobs currently being filled by immigrants flocking to Britain. He put a new emphasis on 'Britishness' at the heart of his programme for government.

'It is time to train British workers for the British jobs that will be available over the coming few years and to make sure that people who are inactive and unemployed are able to get the new jobs on offer in our country', Mr Brown told the GMB union. He said he wanted to sign partnerships with all the major industries that they would help British workers to access the jobs that were available. The government has faced growing complaints that a new wave of immigrants from countries such as Poland and Romania is driving down wages and reducing job opportunities for domestic workers.

Ruth Kelly, the Communities Secretary, and Liam Byrne, the Home Office minister, have called for a national 'Britain Day' to promote pride in our country and prevent communities fracturing under the weight of unprecedented immigration. They suggested the national day could coincide with the annual State Opening of Parliament and be accompanied by a US-style State of the Nation address by the Prime Minister.

The day would be the centrepiece of plans to accelerate the 'citizenship revolution' in Britain. The ministers envisage immigrants being issued with 'good neighbour contracts', which set out their rights and duties in their new home. Foreigners applying to become British citizens would be required to 'win' citizenship points — earning credits for civic or voluntary work and losing credits if they broke the law or spent too long abroad.

David Cameron, the Conservative leader, said that Britain had failed to create a sense of common identity accepted by all its citizens. He warned that Britain was facing a growing problem of 'cultural separatism', where the next generation of British Muslims were more separate from mainstream opinion than their parents. He told a conference on Islam in London that 31% of Muslims in this country felt they had more in common with Muslims abroad than with non-Muslims in Britain.

'There is something much deeper at work here: a feeling of alienation. A disillusionment with life in this country.'

Adapted from the *Telegraph*, 6 June 2007 **www.telegraph.co.uk/news/main.jhtml?xml=/news/2007/06/06/nbrown106.xml**

Document 2: British, migrant, white, black — workers, unite!

At the end of last month, after the government admitted that it had underestimated the number of migrant workers in Britain by hundreds of thousands, Gordon Brown tried to fight back with a straightforward appeal to xenophobic bigotry. 'British jobs for British workers', a slogan used by the BNP in the 1980s and the NF in the 1970s, became an official part of government policy.

The Queen's Speech (6 November) announced a new 'points system' for migrants from outside the European Union. This means that people with wealth, or advanced qualifications of the sort more easily gained by those from a well-off family background, get in. The less well-off are kept out. There will be a compulsory English test. You will be tested if you come from Colombia or India, but not if you come from France or Sweden. This has rightly been dubbed 'lace curtain racism'. (It also comes at a time when the government is cutting English as a second language provision.) The left must condemn Brown's appeal to bigotry and New Labour's hypocrisy.

As a party which serves the British capitalist class, New Labour wants more migrant labour in Britain — skilled and unskilled. That is why most new jobs created here since 1997 have gone to migrant workers. 'British jobs for British workers' is demagogy and it would be illegal under EU law to implement such a policy.

What can Brown achieve by the slogan? The denial of proper rights for asylum seekers or of rights which would allow migrant workers to assert their rights and get organised. The government wants a steady flow of migrant labour, but one firmly under capitalist control. At the same time, they aim to appeal to disillusioned white working-class voters, and win the competition with the Tories for 'middle-class' right-wingers. Hence their doublespeak on immigration.

In our counter-attack, the left must be very clear. We must oppose economic nationalism, the points system and language tests. We must demand open borders: the repeal of all anti-immigration and asylum legislation. And we must fight for the labour movement to organise all workers, British-born or migrant, legal or illegal, in resistance to this anti-working-class government.

Adapted from an article by Gerry Bates on the website Workers' Liberty for international working class solidarity and socialism, 17 November 2007 www.workersliberty.org/node/9534

1 Identify the source of Document 1, stating whether it is right- or left-wing.

2 To what extent does the political bias of the newspaper appear to have influenced its stance on immigration?

3 Consider the fact that Gordon Brown made this speech when addressing a large trade union affiliated to the Labour Party. Suggest two criteria that could be used to judge the credibility of this speech, explain how they could be applied and whether they would weaken or strengthen his claims.

4 Use two appropriate credibility criteria to suggest why the *Telegraph* may have chosen to include a speech by Cameron in an article with a headline about Brown. Explain the relevance of the criteria chosen and state whether they weaken or strengthen the credibility of the document.

5 Compare Cameron's comments on threats to Britain's unity with Brown's. Is there conflict, corroboration or neither? Explain your answer.

6 Identify the source of Document 2, stating whether it is right- or left-wing.

7 To what extent has its political bias influenced its views on immigration and attitude to the government?

8 To what extent is the use of language likely to affect readers' assessment of the source? Include quotations in your answer.

9 What evidence does Document 2 provide that Gordon Brown might not be sincere in his request for 'British jobs for British workers'?

10 According to the writer, what might be Brown's motivation for making use of such a slogan?

11 Compare what is said or implied about the position of non-British residents in the UK in the two documents, identifying several examples of conflict and corroboration and supporting your answer with quotations from the documents.

Section 2: Credibility
Evaluating visual material

Some of the documents you encounter in the Unit 1 examination may be accompanied by photographs, drawings or graphs. There are likely to be questions asking you to assess the degree to which these images or their accompanying captions support the claims being made.

Depending on the situation, you may need to consider whether a photograph could have been faked, manipulated or cropped to suggest an event that did not really happen. Alternatively, it may be too blurred for you to be certain what is being shown, or the focus might be too narrow to give an impression of the scale of the object or to show the surrounding context. It may be that the camera angle or lighting makes people look particularly threatening or that an untypical view has been taken to give the impression that a holiday resort is more beautiful than it really is. In a recent examination paper, photographs of what was claimed to be pock-marked moon rock could easily have been faked using rocks from Earth, and a photograph of an astronaut stepping on to the moon was both indistinct and taken from an improbable angle.

Cartoons or artist's impressions need to be examined for the attitudes portrayed and to see how accurately they reflect the facts in the passage. An artist's impression of lowering lifeboats from a ship may bear little resemblance to the real situation of panic as the *Titanic* was sinking.

In the case of graphs, charts or statistics, it is important to look closely at exactly what is being measured and the units employed, as the information may conflict with the claims in the passage, be irrelevant, selective or out of date.

Scrutinise the captions accompanying illustrations. In newspapers there is a tendency for the caption to convey a simpler message than the article itself. Though this may be for reasons of brevity, it is nevertheless misleading and therefore worthy of mention in your assessment.

The exercise below provides some quick practice in the assessment of illustrations and their accompanying captions, but it is important to get used to evaluating visual material accompanying an article by looking at examination papers.

Exercise 13

For each photograph, assess how convincingly it supports the accompanying caption, giving reasons for your answer.

1

Monster sighted in Loch Ness

2

The UFO seen above Farnborough today

3

PAT MORRIS/ARDEA.COM

A giant rodent thought to be new to science has been discovered in a remote mountainous area of Indonesia

....

....

....

....

....

....

4 What important information is missing from the graph below?

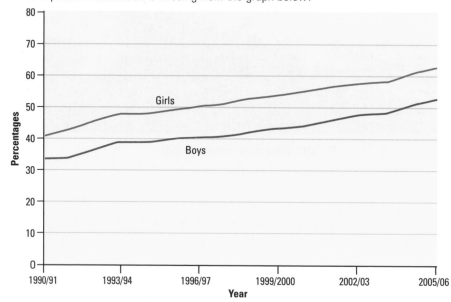

Girls continue to outperform boys in education

Source: National Statistics Online

Section 3:
Specimen examination paper

Time 1 hour 30 minutes. Total number of marks for this paper is 75. The marks for each question are given in brackets.

You are advised to spend about 30 minutes of the examination time on Section A and about 45 minutes on Section B.

Read the documents before starting to answer the questions.

Section A: The language of reasoning

Read the document **'Cannabis smoking, a cause for concern'** on pp. 48–49 and answer all the following questions.

1 Identify the main conclusion of the argument presented in the passage. (2 marks)

2 Identify the reason in paragraph 1 that is given to support the main conclusion. (3 marks)

3 In paragraph 2 the author begins, 'Although the average tobacco user smokes more than a cannabis user'.

a Identify what component of the argument this is. (2 marks)

b Explain your decision. (2 marks)

4 Identify the reason in paragraph 3 that is given to support the main conclusion.　　　(3 marks)

....

....

5 Identify the hypothetical reasoning used in paragraph 4.　　　(2 marks)

....

....

6 Identify three strengths in the evidence provided in paragraph 1.　　　(6 marks)

....

....

....

....

....

....

7 Suggest two possible weaknesses in the evidence in paragraph 4 that 'a sixth of 15- to 34-year-olds have tried cannabis in the past year, making it the most commonly used drug'.　　　(4 marks)

....

....

....

....

8 a To support the reasoning in the final sentence of paragraph 4, what must the author assume about the survey mentioned in the second and third sentences of the paragraph?　　　(2 marks)

....

....

....

....

b Explain your answer. (2 marks)

....

....

....

....

9 Identify the reason in paragraph 5 that is given to support the main conclusion. (3 marks)

....

....

10 In paragraph 5 it is stated that the New Zealand scientists felt confident that the higher incidence of psychotic symptoms among cannabis users was not likely to be due to people with mental illnesses having a greater wish to smoke cannabis. Identify evidence in this paragraph that supports this view and explain your answer. (4 marks)

....

....

....

....

....

Section A total: 35 marks

Cannabis smoking, a cause for concern

1 The public must be warned that smoking cannabis may carry even greater physical and mental health risks than smoking tobacco. Inhaled cannabis smoke is more toxic. Canada's health research department recently found 20 times as much ammonia and five times as much hydrogen cyanide and nitrogen oxides, linked to cancer, heart and lung damage respectively, in cannabis smoke than in tobacco smoke, *New Scientist* said. Researchers used a smoking machine to analyse the smoke for nearly 20 harmful chemicals.

2 Although the average tobacco user smokes more than a cannabis user, previous research shows cannabis smoke is more harmful to lungs than tobacco smoke; it is inhaled more deeply and held in the lungs for longer.

3 Because it is an illegal substance, the content of cannabis is much harder to regulate than the content of tobacco. Dr Richard Russell, a specialist, said: 'Tobacco from manufacturers is cleaned, whereas cannabis is relatively unprocessed and therefore more toxic.'

4 About a quarter of the UK population smokes tobacco products, while a sixth of 15- to 34-year-olds have tried cannabis in the past year, making it the most commonly used drug. Recent surveys show that 79% of children believed that cannabis was 'safe'. Only 2% knew of health risks associated with smoking. If young people are misinformed about the dangers of cannabis, then uptake could increase, with disastrous results to health.

5 Smoking cannabis is thought to double the risk of developing serious mental illnesses such as schizophrenia. New Zealand scientists suggest the probable cause is resulting chemical changes in the brain. They followed over 1,000 people born in 1977 for 25 years, interviewing them about various aspects of their mental health and their cannabis use at the ages of 18, 21 and 25. Psychotic symptoms were more common among cannabis users. Findings were analysed to explore the possibility that mental illness encouraged people to use more cannabis, rather than the drug contributing to their condition, but researchers ruled this out. Even when all factors, such as family history, were taken into account, there was a clear increase in psychotic symptoms after regular use began.

6 The charity SANE welcomed confirmation of the link between cannabis and psychosis, urging the government to reconsider its decision on classification and to launch an education campaign on the dangers of cannabis for young people.

Adapted from two BBC Online sites

http://news.bbc.co.uk/2/hi/health/7150274.stm

http://news.bbc.co.uk/1/hi/health/4305783.stm

Section B: Credibility

Read the document **'Have extraterrestrials visited the Earth?'** on pp. 53–55 and answer all the following questions.

1 Assess how far the extract from the website 'Welcome to the world of Erich von Däniken' is a credible report. You should make two points, identifying and explaining credibility criteria relevant to the source and stating whether they strengthen or weaken its credibility.   (6 marks)

2 Assess the credibility of Legendary Times Books' assessment of Erich von Däniken's work. Refer to one credibility criterion in your answer and explain how this weakens or strengthens credibility. (3 marks)

....

....

....

....

3 Examine von Däniken's claim that the markings in the Peruvian desert could not have been made by primitive men alone. Identify two aspects of the markings that could support this idea and explain your reasoning. (4 marks)

....

....

....

....

....

....

4 Assess the credibility of Maria Reiche. You should make two points, referring to credibility criteria in your answer, explaining their relevance and stating how these may weaken or strengthen her credibility. (6 marks)

....

....

....

....

....

....

....

5 Archaeologists have pointed out the striking similarity between the stylised figures in the Peruvian desert, shown in the illustration, and images on known Nazca artefacts such as pottery. If true, does this lend more support to von Däniken's or Reiche's theory about the desert markings? Explain your answer. (2 marks)

6 Look at the photograph on p. 54 of the stone slab from Palenque, Mexico, and accompanying caption. Assess their usefulness in supporting von Däniken's theory that advanced extraterrestrials have visited the Earth. (2 marks)

7 Paragraph 7 refers to von Däniken's claim that the Easter Islanders did not have the technology to carve and erect the massive statues themselves, so they must have been created by extraterrestrials. Assess the reasonableness of this claim with reference to material from the passage. (4 marks)

8 Look at the image of the Easter Island statues and accompanying caption (p. 55). Assess their usefulness in supporting von Däniken's claim about the origin of the statues. (2 marks)

9 Look at the claims Sheaffer says von Däniken made in an interview with the *National Enquirer* and compare them with von Däniken's claims described in paragraphs 4, 6 and 7. How do the claims mentioned by Sheaffer differ in nature from the others? (2 marks)

10 Drawing on paragraphs 1, 2 and 8, make three developed points that compare and contrast the relative plausibility of Erich von Däniken and Robert Sheaffer, using appropriate credibility criteria. Then make an overall assessment of the quality of the evidence in order to reach a final judgement about which is the more credible. (9 marks)

Section B: total 40 marks

Total for paper: 75 marks

Have extraterrestrials visited the Earth?

1 'For over 40 years, Swiss author **Erich von Däniken** has pursued the theory which postulates that Earth might have been visited by extraterrestrials in the remote past. Born on 14 April 1935 in Switzerland, he was educated at the College St-Michel in Fribourg, where he occupied his time with the study of ancient holy writings. While managing director of a Swiss 5-star hotel, he wrote his first book, *Chariots of the Gods?*, which was an immediate bestseller in the USA, Germany, and later in 38 other countries.

2 In the USA he won instant fame as a result of the television special *In Search of Ancient Astronauts*, based upon this book. The world's most successful non-fiction writer of all time, he has since written 26 books on the topic of extraterrestrials and has sold over 63 million copies worldwide, translated into 32 languages. Fluent in four languages, Erich von Däniken is an avid researcher and an energetic traveller, averaging 100,000 miles per year to visit remote places of the Earth. This enables him to closely examine the phenomena about which he writes. In 2003 he opened a gigantic "*Mysteries of the World*" theme park in Interlaken, Switzerland.' So reads the website Welcome to the World of Mysteries of Erich von Däniken, in which he includes a link inviting readers to join his Archaeology, Astronautics & SETI Research Association.

Welcome to the World of Mysteries of Erich von Däniken **www.daniken.com/e/index.html**

3 Legendary Times Books, Erich von Däniken's publisher, describes *Chariots of the Gods?* as 'a work of monumental importance, the first book to introduce the shocking theory that ancient Earth had been visited by aliens. It is based upon his lifelong studies of ancient ruins, lost cities, potential spaceports, and a myriad of hard scientific facts that point to extraterrestrial intervention in human history. Most incredible of all is von Däniken's theory that we ourselves are the descendants of these galactic pioneers — and the archaeological discoveries that prove it.'

Legendary Times Books website **www.legendarytimesbooks.com/product.php?productid=178&cat=0&page=1**

4 Several of these 'discoveries' are in South America. In 1939 pilots flying over Nazca in the Peruvian desert noticed strange markings in the sand, consisting of huge birds and animals and very straight lines that are up to 40 miles long. Arguing that such markings could not have been drawn by primitive people alone, von Däniken claims that the lines were a landing strip for extraterrestrials, aided in their construction by flying saucers hovering above and beaming instructions about the positions for the markings down to humans on the ground.

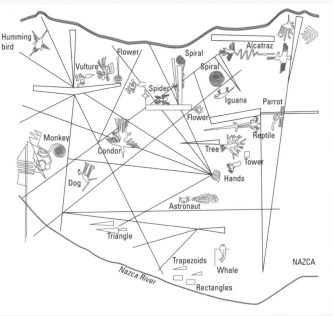

The Nazca markings von Däniken claims were made with extraterrestrial aid

5   Maria Reiche, the German-born mathematician and archaeological researcher who for 50 years has mapped and attempted to preserve the markings, explains that Nazca artists some time between 200 BC and AD 600 prepared preliminary drawings on small six-foot-square plots. These plots are still visible near many of the larger figures. The preliminary drawing was then broken down into its component parts for enlargement. Straight lines, she observed, could be made by stretching a rope between two stakes. Circles could easily be scribed by means of a rope anchored to a rock or stake, and more complex curves could be drawn by linking appropriate arcs. As proof, she reported that there are indeed stones or holes at points that are centres for arcs.

6   A further piece of evidence Erich von Däniken uses to support his theory that extraterrestrials visited us is the carving on a stone slab in the Mayan Temple of Inscriptions at Palenque, Mexico, dated about AD 680. He claims it shows an ancient astronomer working the controls of his space ship.

An ancient astronomer working the controls of his space ship, according to von Däniken

7   Another site of interest to von Däniken is Easter Island in the South Pacific. The island has 250 statues of small-bodied, large-headed men, some of them 30 feet high and weighing 60 tons. The oldest of these statues has been dated at around AD 400. Von Däniken argues that the primitive islanders did not have the technology to carve and erect the massive statues themselves so they must have been created by extraterrestrials. He has made a similar claim about the Egyptian pyramids. Men in the period 2500 BC did not have the tools or knowledge to manipulate the heavy blocks needed to create these massive structures, so only aliens could have done it.

Easter Island statues: too huge to be made by primitive man?

8   Robert Sheaffer disputes von Däniken's theory. On his website he describes himself as 'a freelance writer, and sceptical investigator of all manner of bogus claims' such as Creationism, feminism, the divinity of Christ and extraterrestrialism. A data communications engineer in America's Silicon Valley, Sheaffer has written articles for *Scientific American*, and *Astronomy* magazine, and was a founding member of the UFO Subcommittee of the *Committee for Skeptical Inquiry*, convinced that UFOs are not alien spacecraft. In an article published in *The UFO Investigator* in 1974 he wrote that von Däniken's liking for 'half-truths (as well as quarter and eighth-truths, too)...brought him into conflict with the law. A court in his native Switzerland found von Däniken guilty of embezzlement, forgery, and fraud, sentencing him to three and a half years in prison. While operating a Swiss hotel, it seems he fraudulently obtained money by misrepresenting his financial assets, this experience in deception later proving invaluable in his literary career. It was during this stay as a guest of the Swiss government that he wrote his second book, *Gods from Outer Space*, now also a bestseller.

9   Once a liar, however, does not infallibly prove him always a liar... In fact, we have in support of these theories one bona fide, highly reliable eyewitness who saw these creatures disembark who can now describe it: none other than Erich von Däniken himself! In an exclusive interview with the *National Enquirer*, von Däniken tells of his experiences in Point Aleph, "a sort of fourth dimension" where time doesn't exist. He revealed how he can now leave his body at will, transcending all concepts of space and time. "I know that astronauts visited the earth in ancient times," he confides, because "I was there when the astronauts arrived. And I know they'll be back." Unfortunately for us, he can't say exactly when, since "time doesn't exist in Point Aleph."

'Erich von Däniken's *Chariots of the Gods?*: science or charlatanism?' by Robert Sheaffer, first published in the *NICAP UFO Investigator*, October/November 1974

www.debunker.com/texts/vondanik.html